PERSONAL DETAILS

NAME _____

ADDRESS _____

_____

_____

POSTCODE _____

TELEPHONE _____

WORK _____

MOBILE _____

E-MAIL _____

IN AN EMERGENCY

NAME _____

ADDRESS _____

_____

_____

POSTCODE _____

TELEPHONE _____

WORK _____

MOBILE _____

DOCTOR _____

BLOOD TYPE _____

CONVERSIONS

LENGTH

cm	cm or inches	inches
2.54	1	0.394
5.08	2	0.787
7.62	3	1.181
10.16	4	1.575
12.7	5	1.969
15.24	6	2.362
17.78	7	2.756
20.32	8	3.15
22.86	9	3.543
25.4	10	3.937

CAPACITY

litres	litres or UK gallons	UK gallons
4.546	1	0.22
9.092	2	0.44
13.638	3	0.66
18.184	4	0.88
22.731	5	1.1
27.277	6	1.32
31.823	7	1.54
36.369	8	1.76
40.915	9	1.98
45.461	10	2.2

WEIGHT

kg	kg or lb	lb
0.454	1	2.205
0.907	2	4.409
1.361	3	6.614
1.814	4	8.818
2.268	5	11.023
2.722	6	13.228
3.175	7	15.432
3.629	8	17.637
4.082	9	19.841
4.536	10	22.046

SPEED

mph	20	30	40	50	60	70	80	90	100
km/h	32	48	64	80	96	112	128	144	160

FUEL

gallons	1	2	4	6	8	10	12	14
litres	4.55	9.09	18.18	27.28	36.37	45.46	54.55	63.64

MILES PER GALLON/LITRE

miles per gallon   miles per litre

50 miles to 1 gallon = 11.0 miles to 1 litre

40 miles to 1 gallon = 8.8 miles to 1 litre

30 miles to 1 gallon = 6.6 miles to 1 litre

20 miles to 1 gallon = 4.4 miles to 1 litre

QUICK DISTANCE GUIDE

1 kilometre = 1,094 yards

1 kilometre = approx ⅔ mile

10 kilometres = approx 6¼ miles

100 kilometres = approx 62 miles

TEMPERATURE

°Celsius to °Fahrenheit	°C x 9 ÷ 5 + 32
°Fahrenheit to °Celsius	(°F − 32) x 5 ÷ 9

SPEED CONVERSION

	multiply by
mph to km/h	1.609
km/h to mph	0.621

2022 NOTABLE DATES

JANUARY

1	Sat	New Year's Day
3	Mon	Holiday (UK, R. of Ireland, CAN, AUS, NZL)
4	Tue	Holiday (SCT, NZL)
17	Mon	Martin Luther King, Jr. Day (Holiday USA)
25	Tue	Burns Night (SCT)
26	Wed	Australia Day (Holiday AUS)

FEBRUARY

6	Sun	Waitangi Day (NZL)
7	Mon	Holiday (NZL)
14	Mon	St Valentine's Day
21	Mon	Presidents' Day (Holiday USA)

MARCH

1	Tue	St David's Day
		Shrove Tuesday
2	Wed	Ash Wednesday
13	Sun	Daylight Saving Time begins (USA, CAN)
14	Mon	Commonwealth Day
17	Thu	St Patrick's Day
		(Holiday N. Ireland, R. of Ireland)
27	Sun	Mothering Sunday (UK, R. of Ireland)
		Summer Time begins*

APRIL

3	Sun	Daylight Saving Time ends
		(NZL, AUS – except NT, QLD, WA)
		First Day of Ramadan
15	Fri	Good Friday (Holiday UK, CAN, AUS, NZL)
16	Sat	First Day of Passover (Pesach)
17	Sun	Easter Sunday
18	Mon	Easter Monday (Holiday UK except SCT, R. of Ireland, CAN, AUS, NZL)
22	Fri	Earth Day
23	Sat	St George's Day
25	Mon	Anzac Day (Holiday AUS, NZL)

MAY

2	Mon	Holiday (UK, R. of Ireland)
8	Sun	Mother's Day (USA, CAN, AUS, NZL)
23	Mon	Victoria Day (Holiday CAN)
30	Mon	Memorial Day (Holiday USA)

JUNE

2	Thu	Holiday (UK)
3	Fri	The Queen's Platinum Jubilee (Holiday UK)
6	Mon	Holiday (R. of Ireland)
		Queen's Birthday (Holiday NZL)
19	Sun	Father's Day (UK, R. of Ireland, USA, CAN)

JULY

1	Fri	Canada Day (Holiday CAN)
4	Mon	Independence Day (Holiday USA)
12	Tue	Battle of the Boyne (Holiday N. Ireland)

AUGUST

1	Mon	Holiday (SCT, R. of Ireland)
29	Mon	Holiday (UK except SCT)

SEPTEMBER

4	Sun	Father's Day (AUS, NZL)
5	Mon	Labor Day (Holiday USA)
		Labour Day (Holiday CAN)
21	Wed	UN International Day of Peace
25	Sun	Daylight Saving Time begins (NZL)

OCTOBER

2	Sun	Daylight Saving Time begins (AUS – except NT, QLD, WA)
4	Tue	World Animal Day
10	Mon	Columbus Day (Holiday USA)
		Thanksgiving Day (Holiday CAN)
24	Mon	Labour Day (Holiday NZL)
30	Sun	Summer Time ends*
31	Mon	Hallowe'en
		Holiday (R. of Ireland)

NOVEMBER

5	Sat	Bonfire Night
6	Sun	Daylight Saving Time ends (USA, CAN)
11	Fri	Veterans Day (Holiday USA)
		Remembrance Day (Holiday CAN)
13	Sun	Remembrance Sunday (UK)
24	Thu	Thanksgiving Day (Holiday USA)
30	Wed	St Andrew's Day (Holiday SCT)

DECEMBER

24	Sat	Christmas Eve
25	Sun	Christmas Day
26	Mon	Boxing Day, St Stephen's Day (Holiday UK, R. of Ireland, CAN, AUS, NZL) Holiday (USA)
27	Tue	Holiday (UK, R. of Ireland, CAN, AUS, NZL)
31	Sat	New Year's Eve

2022 CALENDAR

JANUARY

Monday	31	3	10	17	24
Tuesday		4	11	18	25
Wednesday		5	12	19	26
Thursday		6	13	20	27
Friday		7	14	21	28
Saturday	1	8	15	22	29
Sunday	2	9	16	23	30

FEBRUARY

Monday		7	14	21	28
Tuesday	1	8	15	22	
Wednesday	2	9	16	23	
Thursday	3	10	17	24	
Friday	4	11	18	25	
Saturday	5	12	19	26	
Sunday	6	13	20	27	

MARCH

Monday		7	14	21	28
Tuesday	1	8	15	22	29
Wednesday	2	9	16	23	30
Thursday	3	10	17	24	31
Friday	4	11	18	25	
Saturday	5	12	19	26	
Sunday	6	13	20	27	

APRIL

Monday		4	11	18	25
Tuesday		5	12	19	26
Wednesday		6	13	20	27
Thursday		7	14	21	28
Friday	1	8	15	22	29
Saturday	2	9	16	23	30
Sunday	3	10	17	24	

MAY

Monday	30	2	9	16	23
Tuesday	31	3	10	17	24
Wednesday		4	11	18	25
Thursday		5	12	19	26
Friday		6	13	20	27
Saturday		7	14	21	28
Sunday	1	8	15	22	29

JUNE

Monday		6	13	20	27
Tuesday		7	14	21	28
Wednesday	1	8	15	22	29
Thursday	2	9	16	23	30
Friday	3	10	17	24	
Saturday	4	11	18	25	
Sunday	5	12	19	26	

JULY

Monday		4	11	18	25
Tuesday		5	12	19	26
Wednesday		6	13	20	27
Thursday		7	14	21	28
Friday	1	8	15	22	29
Saturday	2	9	16	23	30
Sunday	3	10	17	24	31

AUGUST

Monday	1	8	15	22	29
Tuesday	2	9	16	23	30
Wednesday	3	10	17	24	31
Thursday	4	11	18	25	
Friday	5	12	19	26	
Saturday	6	13	20	27	
Sunday	7	14	21	28	

SEPTEMBER

Monday		5	12	19	26
Tuesday		6	13	20	27
Wednesday		7	14	21	28
Thursday	1	8	15	22	29
Friday	2	9	16	23	30
Saturday	3	10	17	24	
Sunday	4	11	18	25	

OCTOBER

Monday	31	3	10	17	24
Tuesday		4	11	18	25
Wednesday		5	12	19	26
Thursday		6	13	20	27
Friday		7	14	21	28
Saturday	1	8	15	22	29
Sunday	2	9	16	23	30

NOVEMBER

Monday		7	14	21	28
Tuesday	1	8	15	22	29
Wednesday	2	9	16	23	30
Thursday	3	10	17	24	
Friday	4	11	18	25	
Saturday	5	12	19	26	
Sunday	6	13	20	27	

DECEMBER

Monday		5	12	19	26
Tuesday		6	13	20	27
Wednesday		7	14	21	28
Thursday	1	8	15	22	29
Friday	2	9	16	23	30
Saturday	3	10	17	24	31
Sunday	4	11	18	25	

2023 CALENDAR

JANUARY

Monday	30	2	9	16	23
Tuesday	31	3	10	17	24
Wednesday		4	11	18	25
Thursday		5	12	19	26
Friday		6	13	20	27
Saturday		7	14	21	28
Sunday	1	8	15	22	29

FEBRUARY

Monday		6	13	20	27
Tuesday		7	14	21	28
Wednesday	1	8	15	22	
Thursday	2	9	16	23	
Friday	3	10	17	24	
Saturday	4	11	18	25	
Sunday	5	12	19	26	

MARCH

Monday		6	13	20	27
Tuesday		7	14	21	28
Wednesday	1	8	15	22	29
Thursday	2	9	16	23	30
Friday	3	10	17	24	31
Saturday	4	11	18	25	
Sunday	5	12	19	26	

APRIL

Monday		3	10	17	24
Tuesday		4	11	18	25
Wednesday		5	12	19	26
Thursday		6	13	20	27
Friday		7	14	21	28
Saturday	1	8	15	22	29
Sunday	2	9	16	23	30

MAY

Monday	1	8	15	22	29
Tuesday	2	9	16	23	30
Wednesday	3	10	17	24	31
Thursday	4	11	18	25	
Friday	5	12	19	26	
Saturday	6	13	20	27	
Sunday	7	14	21	28	

JUNE

Monday		5	12	19	26
Tuesday		6	13	20	27
Wednesday		7	14	21	28
Thursday	1	8	15	22	29
Friday	2	9	16	23	30
Saturday	3	10	17	24	
Sunday	4	11	18	25	

JULY

Monday	31	3	10	17	24
Tuesday		4	11	18	25
Wednesday		5	12	19	26
Thursday		6	13	20	27
Friday		7	14	21	28
Saturday	1	8	15	22	29
Sunday	2	9	16	23	30

AUGUST

Monday		7	14	21	28
Tuesday	1	8	15	22	29
Wednesday	2	9	16	23	30
Thursday	3	10	17	24	31
Friday	4	11	18	25	
Saturday	5	12	19	26	
Sunday	6	13	20	27	

SEPTEMBER

Monday		4	11	18	25
Tuesday		5	12	19	26
Wednesday		6	13	20	27
Thursday		7	14	21	28
Friday	1	8	15	22	29
Saturday	2	9	16	23	30
Sunday	3	10	17	24	

OCTOBER

Monday	30	2	9	16	23
Tuesday	31	3	10	17	24
Wednesday		4	11	18	25
Thursday		5	12	19	26
Friday		6	13	20	27
Saturday		7	14	21	28
Sunday	1	8	15	22	29

NOVEMBER

Monday		6	13	20	27
Tuesday		7	14	21	28
Wednesday	1	8	15	22	29
Thursday	2	9	16	23	30
Friday	3	10	17	24	
Saturday	4	11	18	25	
Sunday	5	12	19	26	

DECEMBER

Monday		4	11	18	25
Tuesday		5	12	19	26
Wednesday		6	13	20	
Thursday		7	14	21	28
Friday	1	8	15	22	29
Saturday	2	9	16	23	30
Sunday	3	10	17	24	31

2022 PLANNER

JANUARY	FEBRUARY	MARCH
1 S	1 T	1 T
2 S	2 W	2 W
3 M	3 T	3 T
4 T	4 F	4 F
5 W	5 S	5 S
6 T	6 S	6 S
7 F	7 M	7 M
8 S	8 T	8 T
9 S	9 W	9 W
10 M	10 T	10 T
11 T	11 F	11 F
12 W	12 S	12 S
13 T	13 S	13 S
14 F	14 M	14 M
15 S	15 T	15 T
16 S	16 W	16 W
17 M	17 T	17 T
18 T	18 F	18 F
19 W	19 S	19 S
20 T	20 S	20 S
21 F	21 M	21 M
22 S	22 T	22 T
23 S	23 W	23 W
24 M	24 T	24 T
25 T	25 F	25 F
26 W	26 S	26 S
27 T	27 S	27 S
28 F	28 M	28 M
29 S		29 T
30 S		30 W
31 M		31 T

2022 PLANNER

APRIL		MAY		JUNE	
1	F	1	S	1	W
2	S	2	M	2	T
3	S	3	T	3	F
4	M	4	W	4	S
5	T	5	T	5	S
6	W	6	F	6	M
7	T	7	S	7	T
8	F	8	S	8	W
9	S	9	M	9	T
10	S	10	T	10	F
11	M	11	W	11	S
12	T	12	T	12	S
13	W	13	F	13	M
14	T	14	S	14	T
15	F	15	S	15	W
16	S	16	M	16	T
17	S	17	T	17	F
18	M	18	W	18	S
19	T	19	T	19	S
20	W	20	F	20	M
21	T	21	S	21	T
22	F	22	S	22	W
23	S	23	M	23	T
24	S	24	T	24	F
25	M	25	W	25	S
26	T	26	T	26	S
27	W	27	F	27	M
28	T	28	S	28	T
29	F	29	S	29	W
30	S	30	M	30	T
		31	T		

2022 PLANNER

JULY		AUGUST		SEPTEMBER	
1	F	1	M	1	T
2	S	2	T	2	F
3	S	3	W	3	S
4	M	4	T	4	S
5	T	5	F	5	M
6	W	6	S	6	T
7	T	7	S	7	W
8	F	8	M	8	T
9	S	9	T	9	F
10	S	10	W	10	S
11	M	11	T	11	S
12	T	12	F	12	M
13	W	13	S	13	T
14	T	14	S	14	W
15	F	15	M	15	T
16	S	16	T	16	F
17	S	17	W	17	S
18	M	18	T	18	S
19	T	19	F	19	M
20	W	20	S	20	T
21	T	21	S	21	W
22	F	22	M	22	T
23	S	23	T	23	F
24	S	24	W	24	S
25	M	25	T	25	S
26	T	26	F	26	M
27	W	27	S	27	T
28	T	28	S	28	W
29	F	29	M	29	T
30	S	30	T	30	F
31	S	31	W		

2022 PLANNER

OCTOBER

1 S
2 S
3 M
4 T
5 W
6 T
7 F
8 S
9 S
10 M
11 T
12 W
13 T
14 F
15 S
16 S
17 M
18 T
19 W
20 T
21 F
22 S
23 S
24 M
25 T
26 W
27 T
28 F
29 S
30 S
31 M

NOVEMBER

1 T
2 W
3 T
4 F
5 S
6 S
7 M
8 T
9 W
10 T
11 F
12 S
13 S
14 M
15 T
16 W
17 T
18 F
19 S
20 S
21 M
22 T
23 W
24 T
25 F
26 S
27 S
28 M
29 T
30 W

DECEMBER

1 T
2 F
3 S
4 S
5 M
6 T
7 W
8 T
9 F
10 S
11 S
12 M
13 T
14 W
15 T
16 F
17 S
18 S
19 M
20 T
21 W
22 T
23 F
24 S
25 S
26 M
27 T
28 W
29 T
30 F
31 S

DECEMBER 2021

Monday ◗

27

Tuesday

28

Holiday (UK, R. of Ireland, AUS, NZL)

Wednesday

29

Thursday

30

Friday

31

New Year's Eve / Holiday (USA)

JANUARY

Saturday

New Year's Day

1

Sunday ●

2

REMEMBER

JANUARY

Monday
3

Tuesday
4

Wednesday
5

Thursday
6

Friday
7

Saturday

8

Sunday ◑

9

REMEMBER

JANUARY

Monday
10

Tuesday
11

Wednesday
12

Thursday
13

Friday
14

JANUARY

Saturday

15

Sunday

16

REMEMBER

JANUARY

Monday ○   Martin Luther King, Jr. Day (Holiday USA)
17

Tuesday
18

Wednesday
19

Thursday
20

Friday
21

JANUARY

Saturday
22

Sunday
23

REMEMBER

JANUARY

Monday
24

Tuesday ◑
25

Burns Night (SCT)

Wednesday
26

Australia Day (Holiday AUS)

Thursday
27

Friday
28

JANUARY

Saturday
29

Sunday
30

REMEMBER

JAN / FEB

Monday
31

Tuesday ●
1

Wednesday
2

Thursday
3

Friday
4

FEBRUARY

Saturday
5

Sunday
6

Waitangi Day (NZL)

REMEMBER

FEBRUARY

Monday
7

Tuesday ◑
8

Wednesday
9

Thursday
10

Friday
11

FEBRUARY

REMEMBER

FEBRUARY

Monday
14

Tuesday
15

Wednesday   ○
16

Thursday
17

Friday
18

FEBRUARY

Saturday
19

Sunday
20

REMEMBER

FEBRUARY

Monday
21

Tuesday
22

Wednesday ◑
23

Thursday
24

Friday
25

FEBRUARY

Saturday
26

Sunday
27

REMEMBER

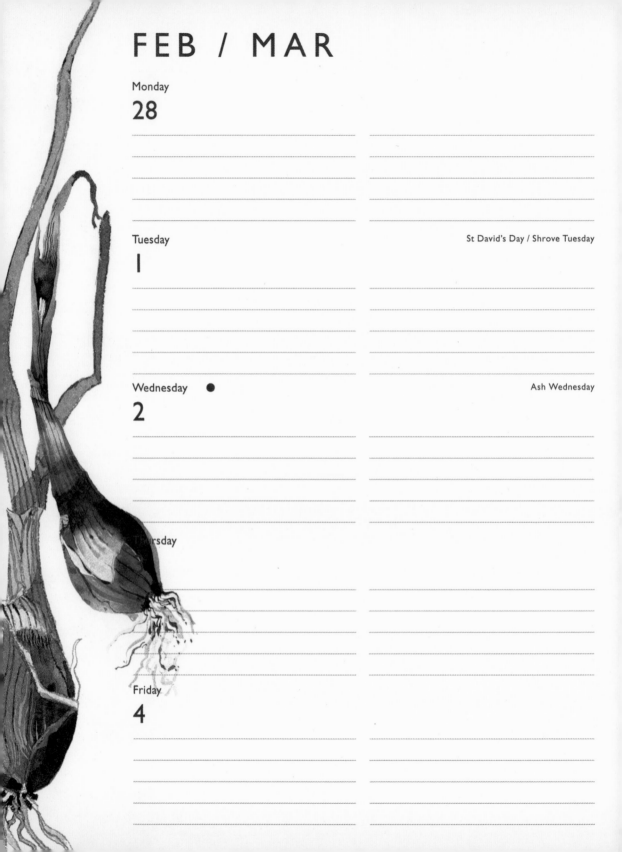

FEB / MAR

Monday
28

Tuesday
1   St David's Day / Shrove Tuesday

Wednesday ●   Ash Wednesday
2

Thursday

Friday
4

Saturday
5

Sunday
6

REMEMBER

MARCH

Monday
7

Tuesday
8

Wednesday
9

Thursday ◑
10

Friday
11

Saturday
12

Sunday
13

Daylight Saving Time begins (USA, CAN)

REMEMBER

MARCH

Monday

14

Commonwealth Day

Tuesday

15

Wednesday

16

Thursday

17

St Patrick's Day (Holiday N. Ireland, R. of Ireland)

Friday ○

18

Saturday
19

Sunday
20

REMEMBER

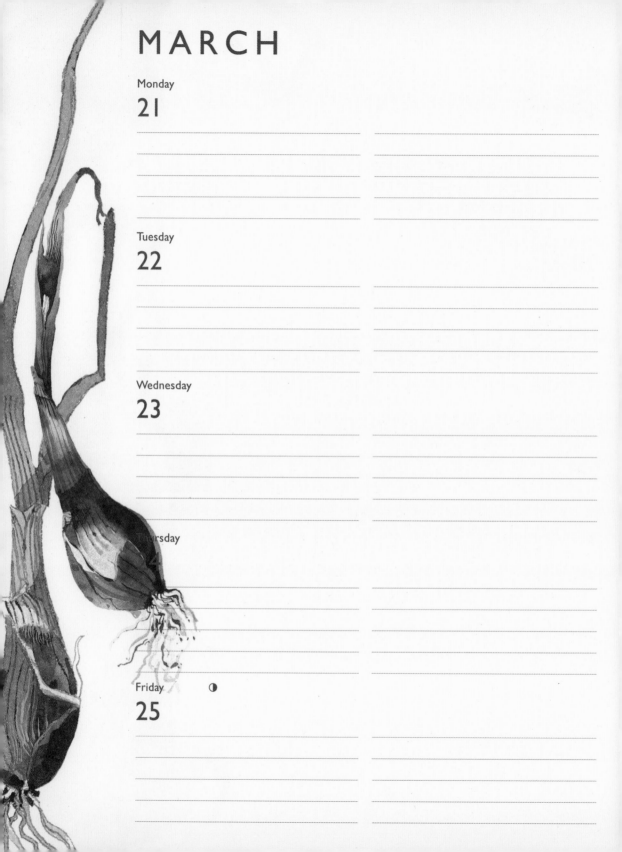

MARCH

Monday
21

_____

_____

_____

_____

Tuesday
22

_____

_____

_____

_____

Wednesday
23

_____

_____

_____

_____

Thursday
4

_____

_____

Friday   ◑
25

_____

_____

_____

_____

Saturday
26

Sunday
27

Mothering Sunday (UK, R. of Ireland) / Summer Time begins*

REMEMBER

MAR / APR

Monday
28

Tuesday
29

Wednesday
30

Thursday
31

Friday
1

APRIL

Saturday
2

Sunday
3

Daylight Saving Time ends (NZL, AUS – except NT, QLD, WA) / First Day of Ramadan

REMEMBER

APRIL

Monday
4

Tuesday
5

Wednesday
6

Thursday
7

Friday
8

APRIL

Saturday ◑
9

_____
_____
_____
_____
_____

Sunday
10

_____
_____
_____
_____

REMEMBER

APRIL

Monday
11

Tuesday
12

Wednesday
13

Thursday
14

Friday
15

Good Friday (Holiday UK, CAN, AUS, NZL)

APRIL

Saturday ○

16

Sunday

17

REMEMBER

APRIL

Monday
18

Tuesday
19

Wednesday
20

Thursday
21

Friday
22

Earth Day

APRIL

Saturday ◑

23

Sunday

24

REMEMBER

APRIL

Monday
25

Tuesday
26

Wednesday
27

Thursday
28

Friday
29

Saturday ●
30

Sunday
1

REMEMBER

MAY

Monday

2

Tuesday

3

Wednesday

4

Thursday

5

Friday

6

Saturday

7

Sunday

8

Mother's Day (USA, CAN, AUS, NZL)

REMEMBER

MAY

Monday ◐
9

Tuesday
10

Wednesday
11

Thursday
12

Friday
13

Saturday

14

Sunday

15

REMEMBER

MAY

Monday   ○
16

Tuesday
17

Wednesday
18

Thursday
19

Friday
20

Saturday
21

Sunday ◑
22

REMEMBER

MAY

Monday
23

Tuesday
24

Wednesday
25

Thursday
26

Friday
27

Saturday
28

Sunday
29

REMEMBER

MAY / JUN

Monday ●

Memorial Day (Holiday USA)

30

Tuesday

31

Wednesday

1

Thursday

Holiday (UK)

2

Friday

The Queen's Platinum Jubilee (Holiday UK)

3

JUNE

Saturday

4

Sunday

5

REMEMBER

JUNE

Monday

6

Holiday (R. of Ireland) / Queen's Birthday (Holiday NZL)

Tuesday ◑

7

Wednesday

8

Thursday

9

Friday

10

JUNE

Saturday

11

Sunday

12

REMEMBER

JUNE

Monday

13

Tuesday ○

14

Wednesday

15

Thursday

16

Friday

17

Saturday
18

Sunday
19

Father's Day (UK, R. of Ireland, USA, CAN)

REMEMBER

JUNE

Monday
20

Tuesday
21

Wednesday
22

Thursday
23

Friday
24

JUNE

Saturday
25

Sunday
26

REMEMBER

JUN / JUL

Monday
27

Tuesday
28

Wednesday ●
29

Thursday
30

Friday
1

Canada Day (Holiday CAN)

Saturday

2

Sunday

3

REMEMBER

JULY

Monday
4

Tuesday
5

Wednesday
6

Thursday   ◑
7

Friday
8

Saturday

9

Sunday

10

REMEMBER

JULY

Monday
11

Tuesday
12

Battle of the Boyne (Holiday N. Ireland)

Wednesday ○
13

Thursday
14

Friday
15

Saturday
16

Sunday
17

REMEMBER

JULY

Monday
18

Tuesday
19

Wednesday ◑
20

Thursday
21

Friday
22

Saturday

23

Sunday

24

REMEMBER

JULY

Monday
25

Tuesday
26

Wednesday
27

Thursday ●
28

Friday
29

Saturday
30

Sunday
31

REMEMBER

AUGUST

Monday
1

Tuesday
2

Wednesday
3

Thursday
4

Friday   ◑
5

Saturday

6

Sunday

7

REMEMBER

AUGUST

Monday
8

Tuesday
9

Wednesday
10

Thursday
11

Friday   ○
12

Saturday

13

Sunday

14

REMEMBER

AUGUST

Monday
15

Tuesday
16

Wednesday
17

Thursday
18

Friday
19

AUGUST

Saturday
20

Sunday
21

REMEMBER

AUGUST

Monday
22

Tuesday
23

Wednesday
24

Thursday
25

Friday
26

AUGUST

Saturday ●
27

Sunday
28

REMEMBER

AUG / SEP

Monday

29

Tuesday

30

Wednesday

31

Thursday

1

Friday

2

SEPTEMBER

Saturday   ◑
3

Sunday
4

Father's Day (AUS, NZL)

REMEMBER

SEPTEMBER

Monday
5

Labor Day (Holiday USA) / Labour Day (Holiday CAN)

Tuesday

Wednesday
7

Thursday
8

Friday
9

SEPTEMBER

Saturday ○
10

Sunday
11

REMEMBER

SEPTEMBER

Monday

12

Tuesday

13

Wednesday

14

Thursday

15

Friday

16

SEPTEMBER

Saturday   ◑
17

Sunday
18

REMEMBER

SEPTEMBER

Monday
19

Tuesday
20

Wednesday
21

UN International Day of Peace

Thursday
22

Friday
23

SEPTEMBER

Saturday
24

Sunday ●
25

Daylight Saving Time begins (NZL)

REMEMBER

SEPTEMBER

Monday
26

Tuesday
27

Wednesday
28

Thursday
29

Friday
30

OCTOBER

1

Sunday
2

Daylight Saving Time begins (AUS – except NT, QLD, WA)

REMEMBER

OCTOBER

Monday ◑

3

Tuesday

4

World Animal Day

Wednesday

5

Thursday

6

Friday

7

OCTOBER

Saturday

8

Sunday ○

9

REMEMBER

OCTOBER

Monday
10

Columbus Day (Holiday USA) / Thanksgiving Day (Holiday CAN)

Tuesday
11

Wednesday
12

Thursday
13

Friday
14

OCTOBER

Saturday
15

Sunday
16

REMEMBER

OCTOBER

Monday ◐
17

Tuesday
18

Wednesday
19

Thursday
20

Friday
21

OCTOBER

Saturday

22

Sunday

23

REMEMBER

OCTOBER

Monday
24

Tuesday ●
25

Wednesday
26

Thursday
27

Friday
28

OCTOBER

Saturday

29

Sunday

30

Summer Time ends*

REMEMBER

OCT / NOV

Monday
3l

Tuesday ☽
1

Wednesday
2

Thursday
3

Friday
4

Saturday

5

Bonfire Night

Sunday

6

Daylight Saving Time ends (USA, CAN)

REMEMBER

NOVEMBER

Monday
7

Tuesday ○
8

Wednesday
9

Thursday
10

Friday   Veterans Day (Holiday USA) / Remembrance Day (Holiday CAN)
11

NOVEMBER

Saturday

12

Sunday

13

Remembrance Sunday (UK)

REMEMBER

NOVEMBER

Monday
14

Tuesday
15

Wednesday ◐
16

Thursday
17

Friday
18

NOVEMBER

Saturday
19

Sunday
20

REMEMBER

NOVEMBER

Monday
21

Tuesday
22

Wednesday ●
23

Thursday
24

Thanksgiving Day (Holiday USA)

Friday
25

NOVEMBER

Saturday
26

Sunday
27

REMEMBER

NOV / DEC

Monday

28

Tuesday

29

Wednesday ◐

30

St Andrew's Day (Holiday SCT)

Thursday

1

Friday

2

DECEMBER

Saturday
3

Sunday
4

REMEMBER

DECEMBER

Monday

5

Tuesday

6

Wednesday

7

Thursday   ○

8

Friday

9

DECEMBER

Saturday
10

Sunday
11

REMEMBER

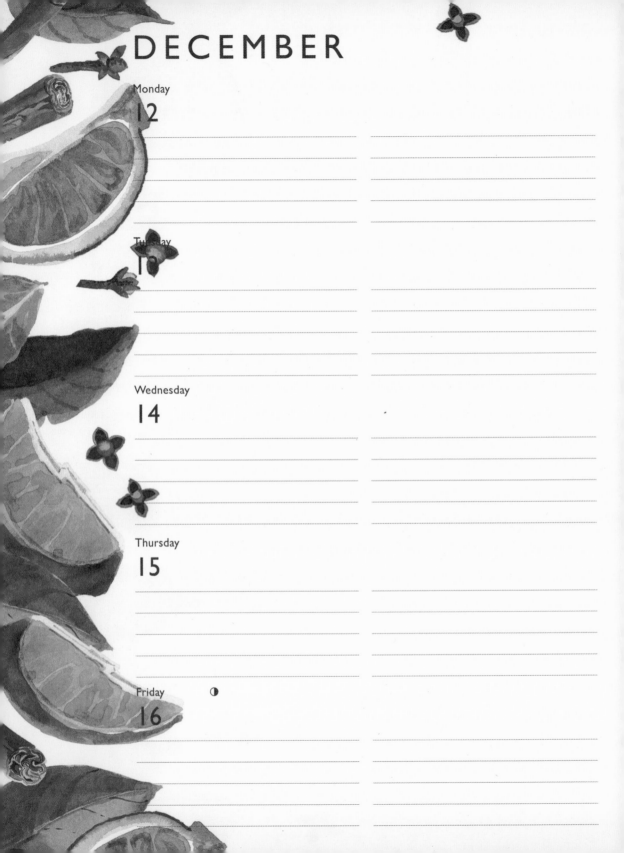

DECEMBER

Monday
12

Tuesday
13

Wednesday
14

Thursday
15

Friday   ◑
16

DECEMBER

Saturday

17

Sunday

18

REMEMBER

DECEMBER

Monday
19

Tuesday
20

Wednesday
21

Thursday
22

Friday
23

DECEMBER

Saturday
24

Sunday
25

Christmas Day

REMEMBER

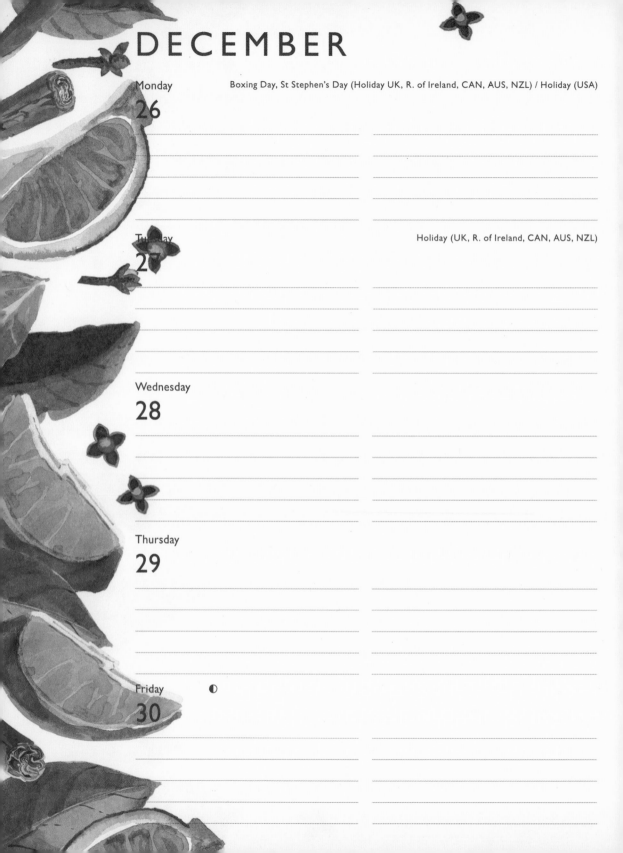

DECEMBER

Monday
26
Boxing Day, St Stephen's Day (Holiday UK, R. of Ireland, CAN, AUS, NZL) / Holiday (USA)

Tuesday
27
Holiday (UK, R. of Ireland, CAN, AUS, NZL)

Wednesday
28

Thursday
29

Friday ◐
30

DEC '22 / JAN '23

Saturday

31

Sunday

1

New Year's Day

REMEMBER

2023 PLANNER

JANUARY

1	S
2	M
3	T
4	W
5	T
6	F
7	S
8	S
9	M
10	T
11	W
12	T
13	F
14	S
15	S
16	M
17	T
18	W
19	T
20	F
21	S
22	S
23	M
24	T
25	W
26	T
27	F
28	S
29	S
30	M
31	T

FEBRUARY

1	W
2	T
3	F
4	S
5	S
6	M
7	T
8	W
9	T
10	F
11	S
12	S
13	M
14	T
15	W
16	T
17	F
18	S
19	S
20	M
21	T
22	W
23	T
24	F
25	S
26	S
27	M
28	T

MARCH

1	W
2	T
3	F
4	S
5	S
6	M
7	T
8	W
9	T
10	F
11	S
12	S
13	M
14	T
15	W
16	T
17	F
18	S
19	S
20	M
21	T
22	W
23	T
24	F
25	S
26	S
27	M
28	T
29	W
30	T
31	F

2023 PLANNER

APRIL

1 S
2 S
3 M
4 T
5 W
6 T
7 F
8 S
9 S
10 M
11 T
12 W
13 T
14 F
15 S
16 S
17 M
18 T
19 W
20 T
21 F
22 S
23 S
24 M
25 T
26 W
27 T
28 F
29 S
30 S

MAY

1 M
2 T
3 W
4 T
5 F
6 S
7 S
8 M
9 T
10 W
11 T
12 F
13 S
14 S
15 M
16 T
17 W
18 T
19 F
20 S
21 S
22 M
23 T
24 W
25 T
26 F
27 S
28 S
29 M
30 T
31 W

JUNE

1 T
2 F
3 S
4 S
5 M
6 T
7 W
8 T
9 F
10 S
11 S
12 M
13 T
14 W
15 T
16 F
17 S
18 S
19 M
20 T
21 W
22 T
23 F
24 S
25 S
26 M
27 T
28 W
29 T
30 F

2023 PLANNER

JULY		AUGUST		SEPTEMBER	
1	S	1	T	1	F
2	S	2	W	2	S
3	M	3	T	3	S
4	T	4	F	4	M
5	W	5	S	5	T
6	T	6	S	6	W
7	F	7	M	7	T
8	S	8	T	8	F
9	S	9	W	9	S
10	M	10	T	10	S
11	T	11	F	11	M
12	W	12	S	12	T
13	T	13	S	13	W
14	F	14	M	14	T
15	S	15	T	15	F
16	S	16	W	16	S
17	M	17	T	17	S
18	T	18	F	18	M
19	W	19	S	19	T
20	T	20	S	20	W
21	F	21	M	21	T
22	S	22	T	22	F
23	S	23	W	23	S
24	M	24	T	24	S
25	T	25	F	25	M
26	W	26	S	26	T
27	T	27	S	27	W
28	F	28	M	28	T
29	S	29	T	29	F
30	S	30	W	30	S
31	M	31	T		

2023 PLANNER

OCTOBER		NOVEMBER		DECEMBER	
1	S	1	W	1	F
2	M	2	T	2	S
3	T	3	F	3	S
4	W	4	S	4	M
5	T	5	S	5	T
6	F	6	M	6	W
7	S	7	T	7	T
8	S	8	W	8	F
9	M	9	T	9	S
10	T	10	F	10	S
11	W	11	S	11	M
12	T	12	S	12	T
13	F	13	M	13	W
14	S	14	T	14	T
15	S	15	W	15	F
16	M	16	T	16	S
17	T	17	F	17	S
18	W	18	S	18	M
19	T	19	S	19	T
20	F	20	M	20	W
21	S	21	T	21	T
22	S	22	W	22	F
23	M	23	T	23	S
24	T	24	F	24	S
25	W	25	S	25	M
26	T	26	S	26	T
27	F	27	M	27	W
28	S	28	T	28	T
29	S	29	W	29	F
30	M	30	T	30	S
31	T			31	S

2023 NOTABLE DATES

JANUARY

1	Sun	New Year's Day
2	Mon	Holiday (UK, R. of Ireland, USA, CAN, AUS, NZL)
3	Tue	Holiday (SCT, NZL)
16	Mon	Martin Luther King, Jr. Day (Holiday USA)
25	Wed	Burns Night (SCT)
26	Thu	Australia Day (Holiday AUS)

FEBRUARY

6	Mon	Waitangi Day (Holiday NZL)
14	Tue	St Valentine's Day
20	Mon	Presidents' Day (Holiday USA)
21	Tue	Shrove Tuesday
22	Wed	Ash Wednesday

MARCH

1	Wed	St David's Day
12	Sun	Daylight Saving Time begins (USA, CAN)
13	Mon	Commonwealth Day
17	Fri	St Patrick's Day (Holiday N. Ireland, R. of Ireland)
19	Sun	Mothering Sunday (UK, R. of Ireland)
23	Thu	First Day of Ramadan
26	Sun	Summer Time begins*

APRIL

2	Sun	Daylight Saving Time ends (NZL, AUS – except NT, QLD, WA)
6	Thu	First Day of Passover (Pesach)
7	Fri	Good Friday (Holiday UK, CAN, AUS, NZL)
9	Sun	Easter Sunday
10	Mon	Easter Monday (Holiday UK except SCT, R. of Ireland, CAN, AUS, NZL)
22	Sat	Earth Day
23	Sun	St George's Day
25	Tue	Anzac Day (Holiday AUS, NZL)

MAY

1	Mon	Holiday (UK, R. of Ireland)
14	Sun	Mother's Day (USA, CAN, AUS, NZL)
22	Mon	Victoria Day (Holiday CAN)
29	Mon	Holiday (UK) Memorial Day (Holiday USA)

JUNE

5	Mon	Holiday (R. of Ireland) Queen's Birthday (Holiday NZL)
18	Sun	Father's Day (UK, R. of Ireland, USA, CAN)

JULY

1	Sat	Canada Day (Holiday CAN)
4	Tue	Independence Day (Holiday USA)
12	Wed	Battle of the Boyne (Holiday N. Ireland)

AUGUST

7	Mon	Holiday (SCT, R. of Ireland)
28	Mon	Holiday (UK except SCT)

SEPTEMBER

3	Sun	Father's Day (AUS, NZL)
4	Mon	Labor Day (Holiday USA) Labour Day (Holiday CAN)
21	Thu	UN International Day of Peace
24	Sun	Daylight Saving Time begins (NZL)

OCTOBER

1	Sun	Daylight Saving Time begins (AUS – except NT, QLD, WA)
4	Wed	World Animal Day
9	Mon	Columbus Day (Holiday USA) Thanksgiving Day (Holiday CAN)
23	Mon	Labour Day (Holiday NZL)
29	Sun	Summer Time ends*
30	Mon	Holiday (R. of Ireland)
31	Tue	Hallowe'en

NOVEMBER

5	Sun	Bonfire Night Daylight Saving Time ends (USA, CAN)
10	Fri	Holiday (USA)
11	Sat	Veterans Day (USA) Remembrance Day (Holiday CAN)
12	Sun	Remembrance Sunday (UK)
23	Thu	Thanksgiving Day (Holiday USA)
30	Thu	St Andrew's Day (Holiday SCT)

DECEMBER

24	Sun	Christmas Eve
25	Mon	Christmas Day (Holiday UK, R. of Ireland, USA, CAN, AUS, NZL)
26	Tue	Boxing Day, St Stephen's Day (Holiday UK, R. of Ireland, CAN, AUS, NZL)
31	Sun	New Year's Eve

NOTES

CONTACTS

CONTACTS

CONTACTS

CONTACTS

When you have finished with this please recycle it

For more information on recycling this product and its packaging, please visit:

www.carouselcalendars.co.uk/recycle

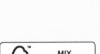

MIX
Paper from responsible sources
FSC™ C007683

Printed In China   220272

CAROUSEL CALENDARS

www.carouselcalendars.co.uk
Exe Box, Matford, Exeter, EX2 8FD
Tel. 01392 826 482
Carousel Calendars is a brand of Vista Stationery & Print Ltd.
Co Registration 5900471.

the great big
CALENDAR
collection

Email sales@gbcc.co.uk